OMANI FOLK TALES

Collected and Written

by

Hatim Al Taie and Joan Pickersgill

Al Roya Press & Publishing House

OMANI FOLK TALES

Publisher
Hatim Al Taie

Al Roya Press & Publishing House
P.O. Box 343, Postal Code 118
Muscat, Sultanate of Oman
Tel: (968) 2456 2138, 2456 2360
Fax: (968) 2456 2194
E-mail: alroya@omantel.net.om

Text
Hatim Al Taie and Joan Pickersgill

Illustrations
James Norton

Design & Production
Dhian C. Bhardwaj

First Edition March, 2008

Printed at Al Anan Printing Press
TeL: (968) 2444 6163

ISBN : 978-9948-03-654-8
103/2008

ACKNOWLEDGEMENTS

To the storytellers of Oman for their patience in recounting the following tales and the enjoyment they gave us in the process we offer sincere thanks. We appreciate the trust they placed in us to record them accurately.

In particular we thank Essa Al Taie, Asma Al Kindi, Hamoud bin Hilal Al Ghifaily, Sheikh Ishaq Al Kindi, Mohammed bin Amer Al Siabi and Sheikh Salem bin Mohamed bib Saqer Al Battahiri.

To George Pickersgill, heartfelt thanks for his confidence in the project and his support in helping us see it through.

To Andrea Davis, thanks for her patient proof-reading.

To the Anglo-Omani Society, many thanks for their support and encouragement to complete the project.

This book is dedicated to the divine
memory of my grandmother
Halima bint Said Al Maashiry

CONTENTS

ONCE UPON A TIME IN OMAN

Oman's oral tradition is very rich and varied but, unfortunately, most of it is undocumented and therefore threatened by the progress of modern culture. With the spread of modernisation throughout the country, the telling of folk tales, among other age-old practices, today represents a dying tradition. Alas, the warm, deep voice of grandmothers telling stories and singing lullabies to their grandchildren before they go to sleep are rapidly being replaced by cold, impersonal cartoons on the television and computer games.

This collection of stories was mainly collected while we were working on *Oman: Comprehensive Guide* in the mid 1990s as we travelled all over the country to record places steeped in history and legend. Today there is an urgent need to work on a national documentation project that aims at recording all aspects of Omani traditional life and its value, from urban planning to the *falaj* system. It is also time to look seriously at preserving the oral asset of the nation. Folk tales, proverbs and oral history are part of a fast-dying ancient traditional culture that is being overtaken by today's fast, aggressive mass media, which is omnipresent due to the availability of satellite television, mobile phones and the Internet.

The selected stories fall into three main categories: the first are related to the supernatural, jinn and magic; the second reflect the power of the Sufi or *Ulama*, whose devotion to God has given them extra powers and respect; and the third are historical and involve Omani heroes who, because of their amazing courage, have been immortalised.

I remember when, as a child, we used to gather at the *sablah* in the village of Bausher and listen to senior and older people talking, discussing issues and chatting over coffee and dates. Once Sheikh Issa, one of the respected older people, burst into tears while listening to my uncle, Sheikh Hashim bin Issa, telling the story of his grandfather who, in a dream, visited paradise where a beautiful angel guarded him. There were thousands of other angels flying around him who showed him his home, which was next to a river of honey and wine. He described, in detail, just how beautiful paradise is. He told the angel that he wanted to stay there forever but was told that he had seven days more on earth before he joined them. While he was telling the story to his family the following day there was a beautiful scent on his hand where he touching the angel, and he believed that it was the scent of paradise. Sheikh Hashim's grandfather died seven days later with the amazing smell still on his hand. Sheikh Issa passed away a month later. I will never forget the tears flowing down his face and white beard.

wwI used to listen to the stories and imagine the fantastic world of the beyond. Storytelling has the power to make the unbelievable believable, the unreal real and the supernatural part of everyday life. But the amazing thing to consider is, was this a true story with the scent as a proof of the visit to paradise?

Folk tales are powerfully imaginative and surpass the limitation of reality we know, and it is this creativity and search for freedom through narration and imagination from which the storyteller creates a world of wonder and interprets it in a fantastic way. Stories that used to be part of everyday life tell of flying carpets, saints performing miracles, talking birds and golden fish speak of wisdom imparted to humans.

The storytellers are from different regions in Oman, and I felt, while listening to them, as if they were reading from the Arabian Nights, although they had never read the book, nor evenheard of those stories, but I can assure you that they come from the same fertile imagination that created those stories.

Storytelling used to be part of everyday life, and the storytellers kept adding appropriate 'flavours' to their stories depending on the audience and their mood. So one can listen to the same story and it would be slightly differently 'spiced' every time. These stories are not fixed, they are dynamic and keep changing constantly like life. They are never perfect but remain unfinished, like love and its endless tragic stories. The story tells itself again and again in different ways, and the storyteller himself becomes supernatural by describing amazing places and creatures, as if he was there. The listener, too, becomes an involved accomplice in the narrative, as someone from the younger generation who has to memorise the story and add to it from his own personal repertoire to keep the tradition alive.

We hope you will enjoy the tales as much as we do.

Hatim al Taie and Joan Pickersgill
Muscat, January 2008

THE BEAUTIFUL WOMAN AND THE SNAKE

The old town of Bowsher nestles in the mountain foothills close to Muscat. Asma Al Kindi, who used to live in Bowsher, told us this tale.

Many long years ago in Bowsher there lived a beautiful lady. Every evening at the same time, at six o'clock, she would go to the *falaj*, a water channel, to bathe in private. One evening she spotted a huge snake watching her. At first she was terrified but the snake seemed to put a spell on her and she was not frightened. Every evening as she disrobed, the snake would appear and it grew bolder and bolder, coming closer and closer. Eventually it began to coil itself around her body, as she stood paralysed.

Now, the woman's husband was a jealous man and she took some time to pluck up courage to tell him about the snake. When she did he took his gun and went to the falaj with her. He lay in wait and as the snake approached his wife he shot it. To his horror both the snake and his wife vanished into thin air immediately.

Distraught, he consulted the local religious man of authority, the *Alim*. This wise man gave him a letter and told him to go to Wadi Al Ghail behind the hot springs of Bou Souman. There he was to wait and give the letter to whomever or whatever approached him.

The wadi was an eerie place but he was so upset by his wife's disappearance that he went. Frightened, he waited and waited through night and day until on the third night a dog appeared. The husband gave the letter to the dog, which started walking backwards to indicate he should follow.

They eventually arrived at a vast and dark cave. At the entrance it seemed deserted but as they went in the husband saw it was like a majlis, a meeting place. It was full of very old people sitting on the floor on cushions. The people were all dressed in white and the men had long white beards. A man approached the husband and took his letter, read it and told him that he had killed one of his sons. The husband realised the cave was full of jinn, spirits, and that the snake must have been one of the jinn. He protested that he had killed a snake not a man. The old man cautioned him and told him never to harm or kill a snake as they might not always be what they appear to be.

When the contrite husband gave his promise never to harm a snake again he was told to leave. On his return home he was overjoyed to find his wife waiting for him.

Hamoud bin Hilal Al Ghifaily told us the next six stories. Hamoud belongs to the younger generation of storytellers. Originally from the eastern Sharqiyah Sands, Hamoud now lives in Mahout on the east coast of Oman.

His first story comes from the east coast town of Sur, the main town in the Sharqiyah Region.

THE BEAUTIFUL WOMAN AND THE MAN WITH THE JEWELS

Once upon a time in Sur there lived a rich man who owned many boats. He had three sons and every year he allowed one of them to take a month off work to go on holiday in one of the boats. It was his eldest son's turn for a holiday and his father reminded him that he must return by the last day of the month. The man was very strict about when his sons had to return and they always obeyed him. He was a good father and always gave his sons jewels to take with them in case they got into trouble and needed money. This time was no exception and he handed his son a purse of rich and sparkling gems.

The son sailed away to a new country and landed in a big city. He had nowhere to stay and as he looked around the market he saw the most elegant and beautiful woman he had ever seen in his life. He was entranced but unsure of how things were done in this country. He did not approach her but followed her to see where she lived. When she went into a large house he asked a person in the street who lived there. They told him it was the home of a city silversmith.

The man from Sur went to the silversmith's shop to try to find out more. He wanted to find out whether the woman was the silversmith's wife or sister, and he hoped to get invited to the house so he could see the beautiful woman again. He decided on a plan; he would ask the silversmith to make him a ring from one of the jewels. He showed the silversmith one of the diamonds he had and asked whether he would make a ring for him. He was clear and precise in the instructions for the ring. The silversmith marvelled at the stone and told him the ring would be ready the next day.

The next day the man told the silversmith that he didn't like the ring. The silversmith was upset and wanted to know why but the man said, "Don't worry I have plenty of jewels. You can keep that ring and make me another."

The silversmith was impressed by this rich man from Sur, particularly when he produced an even finer diamond. The silversmith went home to tell his wife about this man who could afford to give diamonds away. He told his wife that the ring had fitted perfectly but that the man seemed to have money to throw away. They decided to invite him to the house to find out more about him and to see what other riches he had.

When the man went to the shop the next day he pretended he didn't like the second ring that was waiting for him. He produced an even finer stone and told the silversmith, "Do what you like with the ring. I have plenty more jewels."

The silversmith was overjoyed and invited him home. The man from Sur was delighted that his plan was working.

When he arrived at the house, the beautiful woman was waiting and food had been prepared for him. The silversmith had decided to drug the man and search him for jewels, so he turned the part of the dish containing the poisoned food towards the man and urged him to eat. Unsuspecting, the man ate his fill and fell into a deep sleep.

When he woke up, the silversmith introduced the beautiful woman as his wife. There was an instant attraction between the two and the next day a maid from the house delivered a note to him. The beautiful woman told him that her husband would again invite him to come to the house that night. He should accept and she would drug her husband's food so that he would fall asleep. The plan worked and as the husband slept the couple enjoyed their time together.

The next day the maid delivered another message to him. He was to tell the silversmith he was interested in renting a property. There was an empty house next door to the silversmith's home that belonged to a friend who wanted to rent it. If he lived there they would be able to see each other more often. The plan worked well and the Sur man moved in. Between them they dug a tunnel between the houses so that they could see each other without the silversmith suspecting anything.

The Sur man knew the end of the month was not far away and he and his beautiful woman began hatching a plan. He took the silversmith's curved dagger, his *khanjar*, and went to his shop. "I've just bought this *khanjar*, do you think it's worth the price I paid for it?"

"But this is my *khanjar* — I would know it anywhere. It's a fine *khanjar* and worth what you paid for it, but it's mine. It must have been stolen from my house." The silversmith said that he would check when he got home.

The Sur man rushed back to the house and travelled through the tunnel to replace the *khanjar*. When the silversmith returned home he was really puzzled. "I was sure that *khanjar* was mine but mine's here, so I must be mistaken."

The next day the Sur man went to the shop with the silversmith's maid and asked again for advice. "Do you think she is worth the price I paid for her?"

But the silversmith knew the woman was his maid.

"What are you doing here?" he asked her. The maid kept silent and the Sur man said, "She cannot speak; she can't answer you."

The silversmith said, "Well she seems a bargain, but I must go home and see my own maid. I can't believe that two women can look exactly the same, although this one doesn't seem to be able to speak."

When he got home his maid was cooking in the kitchen and he said, "Well it is amazing two people could look so alike, but you can speak the other maid cannot."

The next day the Sur man again went to the shop. This time he produced the beautiful woman and said, "What do you think of my new wife — do you think she is suitable for me. I want to take her back to Sur with me."

The silversmith reeled with shock and amazement, "This must be my wife, it isn't possible for two women to be so alike. I must go home and check on my wife."

When he got home his wife was there and the man told her of the amazing likeness between herself and the Sur man's new wife. She laughed at the story and told him to relax and not to worry.

The next day the Sur man went to the shop to say goodbye to the silversmith.

"It's the end of the month and I must return to my father. I will take my new *khanjar*, maid and beautiful wife with me."

The silversmith was still reeling from the coincidences and was glad that the man was leaving. So, it was with relief he happily waved goodbye to the man with the jewels, new wife, maid and *khanjar*.

SHLAIWEEH, THE BEDOUIN KNIGHT

Once upon a time there lived a Bedouin knight called Shlaiweeh who was known for his bravery and fighting skills. One day he fought with a man from another tribe and killed him, so the tribe, renowned for their strength and might, threatened to avenge the dead man by killing Shlaiweeh. However, they had to wait for the right opportunity as they were frightened of him.

Days and months passed by, Shlaiweeh's land became arid and his tribe's animals started to die of thirst and hunger. Famine prevailed, and those able to leave for better lands did just that, but, unfortunately, Shlaiweeh was forced to go to his enemy's lands because they were fertile, so he disguised himself and pretended to be stupid. He changed his name to Khubla (imbecile) and his camel's name to Khubaila. He approached the tribe's sheikh for a job, and was made to collect wood and do other mundane tasks. Khubla erected a tent at the edge of the village and lived among the tribe without anyone suspecting his true identity.

Soon, enemies attacked the tribe and stole some of their camels and sheep, so the tribe recruited its finest men to fight back. Khubla begged the sheikh to let him go with the men, and he finally agreed to let him help out with caring for the injured.

When war broke out between the two tribes, Khubla was at the front line. He fought the enemies and caused them to retreat. The tribe was amazed at his strength and skill. When they distributed the booty they gave him an equal share of everything, including sugar, coffee, flour and rice.

Day after day passed and the tribe's rations were depleting rapidly. Khubla was one of the few who had saved some rations, and although not originally from the same tribe, he proved to be very generous, helping the poor to survive.

One fine evening, the sheikh visited Khubla in his tent for the first time. After exchanging traditional pleasantries, the sheikh asked Khubla to tell him where he had come from and what his real name was. In the beginning, Khubla tried to be evasive and denied that he had any other name, but the sheikh demanded to know the truth. After much persuasion Khubla agreed to tell him, but only if the sheikh guaranteed his safety. The sheikh accepted, and Khubla recited this poem:

Asking for my name, I am Shlaiweeh
The knight that sends enemies shivering.

When times are hard, and people forget my deeds,
I leave them and go to better lands.

Then Shlaiweeh asked for pardon that was granted and he left in search of a new home.

THE RAVEN'S PREDICTIONS

Told to Hamoud bin Hilal Al Ghifaily by Abouda Al Wahibiah

One fine afternoon two friends, one clever and the other handsome, were walking on the beach. They came upon a beautiful woman riding a horse and escorted by guards. The friends approached and exchanged glances with the woman. So great was her beauty that they couldn't tear their eyes away from her.

She seemed attracted to the handsome man and signed to him by pointing to her eyes, chest and the centre of her body. He didn't understand what the signs meant, although his friend did.

She wanted the handsome man to go to her home that was a three-month journey away. Soon the girl and guards left, and the friends decided to follow them.

When two months and twenty-seven days had passed, the beautiful woman sent seven of her guards to check if there were any strangers in town. They returned to tell her there were no strangers in town.

The next day she sent five guards on the same mission. They returned without seeing anyone new.

On the third day she sent three guards and they found two strangers, who had just arrived in town. The guards took the strangers to the king's majlis, a meeting house. The majlis had two main gates, one facing towards the king's palace, the other towards the town.

When the king arrived he asked them, "Why have you come to this town, what are you looking for?

The clever man replied, "We are poor and so we came here to find work."

"What kind of work can you do?" asked the king.

"We can be guards," said the clever man.

So the king appointed them. The handsome man guarded the door that looked towards the palace, while the clever man was on the other gate.

At night the beautiful woman visited the handsome man but he was so soundly asleep she couldn't wake him. Leaving, she placed a small knife under his pillow.

In the morning the clever man asked his friend, "Did anybody visit you last night?"

"No," was the reply.

The clever man then told his friend the beautiful girl had visited and left something under his pillow. He warned his friend not to sleep on the second night, as she would visit him again.

His friend was still very tired and when the woman visited on the second night he was asleep again. This time she left a ring under his pillow.

The following morning the clever man asked his friend about the visit to be told, "Nobody visited me last night."

"Look under your pillow," the clever man urged.

The handsome man found the ring, and his friend forced it onto his finger, deliberately wounding him in the process. This was to ensure he would be in pain and would not sleep so soundly the following night.

When the woman returned on the third night he pretended to be asleep and didn't answer her. She took her knife out to kill him but at that moment he caught her hand.

"Didn't you get my messages?" she cried.

"No, I was so tired and sound asleep," he replied.

"I love you," she whispered.

"And I, you. I love you and want to marry you."

They agreed that the next day he would ask her father, the king, for her hand in marriage.

"If my father asks for a dowry ask him for three days to get it together."

The next day the two friends went to ask the king for his daughter's hand. The king, as predicted, asked for a payment of a big box of pure gold and one of silver.

They asked him for three days to meet the demands.

The king's daughter sent her maid to tell the men to sleep in the wadi outside town that night, and she would send them the gold and silver in the morning.

As they returned to town with the gold and silver, they came upon three black ravens that spoke to the clever man.

The first raven said, "If your friend cuts a branch from a tree he will die."

The second raven said, "If he kisses his beloved's left cheek, he will die because it is poisoned."

The third said, "If you tell him this secret, you will die."

On the way to town the handsome man got off his horse to cut a tree branch. His friend quickly stopped him and gave him his stick, "This is for you, you don't have to cut a branch off the tree."

They reached the palace safely and gave the king the dowry. After the wedding the clever man insisted that he should sleep in the same room as the couple. Puzzled they agreed, although they thought it was odd.

At midnight the husband left the room for a moment. As he returned he saw his friend kiss the left-hand cheek of his bride. He was angry but the clever man, now poisoned, immediately became very ill.

The men decided to return to their own town with the beautiful woman. The two friends weren't talking to each other anymore because of the kiss. The beautiful woman visited the clever man regularly as he was ill, but her husband wouldn't go with her. Three months passed, and the clever man asked her to plead with her husband to visit him.

"He must come or he will never understand what has happened. I will die and he will never know," he begged.

The next day, both husband and wife visited. The clever man told them what the three ravens had told him.

As he recounted what the first raven said, his legs became paralysed. When he recounted the second raven's comments, his head became paralysed. When he reached the third raven's comments and revealed the secret he was totally paralysed.

The husband and wife returned home but the wife couldn't sleep. She was tormented by the raven's comments and her sympathies lay with the clever man.

She took a knife and killed her husband.

The next day she went to the *arraffa*, an old lady who predicts the future, and told her the sad story.

The *arraffa* told her, "You are pregnant, in your third month. If the baby lives the clever man will die, but if the baby dies he will live."

Six months later she gave birth to a boy baby that sadly, but as predicted, died.

The clever man's health improved immediately and he was cured, and then they began to live together.

ABU AL JAWARY – THE YOUNG MAN WHO PREFERRED THE COMPANY OF GIRLS

Told to Hamoud bin Hilal Al Ghifaily by Waneeh Al Wahibiah from Sirab

Long ago there was a king who had three sons. He worried about his youngest son who spent all his time in the company of girls.

The king and his sons heard there was another king in a faraway country with a beautiful daughter. Many young men had requested her hand in marriage but she had refused them all. She never spoke and the challenge for the men who wanted to marry her was to get her to utter at least three words, but no one had achieved this.

The eldest son of the first king wanted to try to marry her, so his father agreed and sent him away in a fine boat with many attendants and precious gifts.

When he arrived he presented the king with all the money and gifts and asked him for his daughter's hand in marriage.

The king told him the condition, "If you come to my majlis in the early morning, you have until evening to make my daughter speak. If she doesn't speak at least three words you lose all your money and she can make you work wherever and doing whatever she wants."

The prince agreed and the next day he met the princess but she didn't utter a single word all day. He was ordered to work on a farm ploughing the fields.

Now the second son asked his father if he could go and try. His father agreed, and again he gave him lavish gifts and money to take with him. But the second son had no success either. The princess ordered him to work on the farm with his brother. When the king's third son, known as Abu Jawary, asked his father's permission to follow his brothers he was refused.

"The princess won't like you — all you want to do is play with girls."

Abu Jawary went to his father's ministers and advisors and told them what his father had said. He asked them to go to his father and persuade him to change his mind.

They went to the king, "You are saying this son is useless and will play only with girls. Give him this chance to travel and try his luck and you won't have to see him play with girls again."

The king agreed but this time he only gave him a little money to take and a small boat to travel in.

Abu Jawary travelled to the princess's country to ask the king for his daughter's hand. The king laid down the same conditions, so the next morning he went to the *majlis* where he greeted everyone in a lively and friendly manner.

"I am going to ask you all a question. Whoever answers will get lots of money." The people were excited and said, "Go ahead, we are listening."

"Right. Three brothers have a big farm. The first brother ploughs the land, the second sows the seeds, and the third waters it. The question is who owns the land?"

The king's daughter shouted, "The man who waters it."

But the people objected to Abu Jawary marrying the princess.

He said, "All right, I'll ask another question tomorrow."

The next day he posed the question, "There are three brothers. The first has a book, the second a carpet, and the third perfume. When they opened the book they saw the king's daughter dying, so they took the carpet and flew to her aid. The third brother sprinkled perfume over her and life returned to her body. Who saved her life?"

The king's daughter shouted out, "It was the man who sprinkled perfume."

This time the king approved the marriage.

Abu Jawary's two brothers came to him to ask for their freedom and for permission to return to their own country. He agreed on the condition that he would heat his ring and brand each brother's back with it. Soon the three brothers and the princess left in the small boat. In the dead of night, before they reached their homeland, the two brothers threw Abu Jawary overboard.

When they arrived home their father was very happy with the return of his two sons and the beautiful woman. He ordered celebrations but the beautiful woman went to her room and cried.

God sent the dolphins to help Abu Jawary. They led him to the shore of his home, and when the people found him they cried happily, "Abu Jawary is back."

His wife ran to him and hugged him passionately, but his father was very angry, "Why are you hugging him?"

"He is my husband," she cried happily.

"No, I don't believe it," said the king.

The beautiful woman replied, "Go and look at your other sons' backs. If you don't see the stamp of this ring, you can cut off both our heads."

When he examined his sons he realised what she had said was true, so the king ordered fresh celebrations for the couple and named Abu Jawary his successor.

THE SON OF THE BIRD TRAPPER

Told to Hamoud bin Hilal Al Ghifaily by
Abouda Al Wahibiah from Sinaw

Long ago there lived a boy whose father had died and he didn't know how to make a living. He asked his mother many times, "What was my father's job?"

But she never answered, so one day he asked the same question again, and again she didn't answer, so he decided to go to an old lady for advice. She said, "Tomorrow ask your mother to make you a dish called *asseedah*. When it's ready take a little on your finger when it's still very hot and put it on your mother's palm. It will burn her and then she will tell you your father's job."

He did as the old lady told him and when he put the hot *asseedah* food on his mother's hand she said angrily, "Oh you son of a bird trapper!"

The boy then decided to take up his father's profession. On the first day he caught a dove that laid golden eggs. When the king heard of this he asked the boy to give him the dove, but the boy refused until the king threatened him with death.

On the second day he caught a black raven that told him, "You must free me as I have children and no one will feed them. If you let me go you can take three of my feathers. If you are ever in need, burn one and I will grant you your wish."

The boy freed him and went home with the three feathers. The king's guards were waiting to take him to the king. The king said angrily, "The dove stopped laying golden eggs. Go and get her mate to get her to lay, if you don't I will cut off your hand."

The boy didn't know what to do but as he returned home he remembered the raven's feathers. He burned one and when the raven arrived he told him the sad story. The raven replied, "Go and put the net where I tell you. All the birds will come but don't move until the last bird arrives. That will be the dove's mate."

The boy did as he was told and gave the dove to the king.

The king's ministers suggested that the boy could catch that rare mythical creature, half horse and half woman for them. So the next day the boy was summoned and told "You must bring me this mythical creature or I will cut off your head."

The boy sadly returned home and burned the second feather. When the raven arrived he told him what the king wanted.

"Go to the sidr tree in the wadi. Hang by your hands from the branch and don't move until the creature comes. She will shake the tree to gather the fruits. Jump on her back and hold tight. She will fly up the seven skies and down the seven seas to try to dislodge you but when she stops she will obey you."

It happened exactly as the raven said it would, and when the boy told the creature she must go to the king, she had one condition. The king must place a golden carpet from the beginning of the town up to the palace door.

The king agreed and used all his gold to make the carpet. When the creature arrived with her seven sons they trampled and destroyed the carpet with their hooves as they approached the palace. The king's gold was all gone and as the carpet was destroyed he had not kept his condition.

The boy returned to his normal life but the king and his ministers wouldn't leave him alone. They asked him to get the daughter of the moon or they would behead him.

The boy burned his last feather to get the raven's advice.

The raven said, "Continue walking along this road."

The boy then came across a man counting grains of sand. The boy was surprised and said, "What a difficult job you have there."

The man answered, "It's not as difficult as the job of the boy who nets birds and catches wild creatures."

Surprised the boy answered, "That's me, and I'm going to get the daughter of the rising moon for the king"

They travelled together and stopped by a man who was swallowing the entire sea.

The son of the bird catcher exclaimed, "What a difficult job you have there."

The man replied, "It's not as difficult as the job of the boy who nets birds and catches wild creatures."

The boy answered, "That's me and I'm going to get the daughter of the moon for the king." And they all continued along the road together.

Then they met a man moving mountains. The boy said, "What a difficult job you have there."

The man replied, "Not as difficult as the job of the boy who nets birds and catches wild creatures."

The boy said, "That's me, and I'm going to get the daughter of the moon for the king."

So they all went in search of the daughter of the moon. When they reached a forest they came upon some guards. The three men told him they would take away the sight of the guards so they wouldn't see him.

The boy passed the guards and travelled until he reached the daughter of the moon. He caught her and carried her until he reached home.

The daughter of the moon had a condition to make before she agreed to go the king. She wanted a very large hole dug and a fire lit in it. Whoever could jump the hole would be her husband.

The king agreed and said he would jump first. He jumped and fell into the hole.

Next the minister said he would jump, but he also fell in the hole.

Then it was the boy's turn and when he jumped he reached the other side.

The son of the bird trapper married the daughter of the rising moon. He became the king and they lived happily ever after.

YOUNG AZIZ, THE SON OF HIS UNCLE

Told to Hamoud bin Hilal Al Ghifaily
by a venerable woman from Sinaw

Once upon a time there was a strong and brave man, Aziz, who wasn't popular. One day his sister gave birth to a boy who looked just like him and people began to like Aziz a little more. As the boy was so like his uncle he was known as young Aziz, son of his uncle.

Young Azia grew up to be as brave and strong as his uncle, and then one day big Aziz decided to leave to go to a faraway region. He wanted to take young Aziz with him. Young Aziz agreed but his mother was very sad. She didn't understand why her brother wanted to take young Aziz on such a journey.

Uncle and nephew set off and one night as they travelled big Aziz asked his nephew to go and fetch him dinner. They were in the empty desert at the time and the only person around was an old sorceress.

She was known in the area for her long, long hair that she wound into many balls around her head, and for her huge pendulous breasts.

When young Aziz came across her he flung himself into her arms, kissed her breasts and cried, "I beg your protection, I am your son."

She answered, "You are protected, come close to the fire."

As the sorceress slept young Aziz cut seven balls of hair from her head and filled them with embers from the fire. He then stole the rabbit that was cooking and ran off. When she awoke she sent her seven dogs after him, but whenever one of them got near young Aziz he threw one of the hairballs and the dog raced after the ball and returned to the sorceress. This he did seven times and when the balls were all gone the sorceress told the dogs to stay with her and let him have the rabbit.

When young Aziz reached his uncle he was asleep so young Aziz ate the whole rabbit.

In the morning they passed a very deep water well that was haunted by snakes. Big Aziz told his nephew to fill their water bottles.

Young Aziz went down into the well, killed all the snakes, and filled the leather water bottles. His uncle pulled up the rope with the water bottles and then cut the rope. Young Aziz was stranded down the well.

After some time three beautiful girls arrived and found him. The elder one said, "If you are a Muslim, take my hair and I will rescue you," but her hair did not reach to the bottom of the well. The middle girl said, "Take my hair and try," but her hair wasn't long enough either.

Then the youngest girl tried and her was hair was long enough, so young Aziz climbed out of the well. When they set eyes on each other they immediately fell in love.

The girls asked him to go with them but he said he must follow his uncle.

When he joined his uncle he asked for water but his uncle deliberately dropped the water and young Aziz stayed thirsty.

When he told his uncle about the three beautiful girls his uncle said they should follow them. When they reached the town where the girls lived it was the wedding night of Alia, the youngest girl with whom young Aziz had fallen in love.

Big Aziz told his nephew to go Alia's home and dress in her clothes. Young Aziz was to climb into Alia's bed and his uncle would bring the real Alia to him. Young Aziz followed the plan, and when the bridegroom came he couldn't get near to Alia for two nights. "You are very strong, Alia," he said.

On the third night the groom arrived late and young Aziz was asleep. The groom realised he was a man and taking a knife cut young Aziz's hair and stabbed him in his left leg.

Young Aziz left and found Alia and his uncle fast asleep.

In the morning the bridegroom went to Alia's father, the king and said, "I have married a man not a woman."

"Well, said the king, if we find a man you can cut off my head but if we find a woman we will cut off your head."

The women went and searched for Alia and found her, so they killed her husband.

Meanwhile, uncle and nephew continued on their journey. Young Aziz was bleeding badly and wrote with his blood on his camel saddle that he was wounded and no one would help him. Soon young Aziz fell from his camel and died. His uncle buried him and marked the grave by breaking young Aziz's sword in half and placing it into the ground.

When he returned home his sister saw he was alone. She sent the elder of her three daughters to ask him about her son.

"Uncle, where is young Aziz?"

"He went to Al Basra souq and he will be home later. Here is a present for you, a mirror and comb."

The middle daughter went to her uncle. "Uncle, where is young Aziz?"

"He went to Al Basra souq and he will come home later. Here is a present for you, a mirror and comb."

When the youngest daughter went to her uncle to ask the same question she saw young Aziz's camel bag and what he had written on it.

"You are lying, Uncle. You killed my brother." She threw the mirror and comb at him and went crying to her mother.

Alia, daughter of the king, went searching for her love, young Aziz, with her maidservant. When she found his grave she flung herself on top of it and cried and sobbed until she too died. So her maidservant buried Alia near young Aziz's grave.

The following three tales are told by Mohammed bin Amer Al Siabi who lives near Nakhal and belongs to a dwindling group of semi-nomadic shepherds, called *shawawi*. They live on the fringes of modern society but shun modern material benefits in favour of maintaining their traditional values and way of life.

THE FROZEN DATES

Long ago, Imam Shathan was renowned around Nakhal and throughout the rest of Oman for being a just and generous Imam. He was a wealthy man and his knowledge of Islam was immense.

One day, a *shawii* from a nearby village in Wadi Mistel, paid the Imam a visit. He asked the Imam to store a sack of Naghal dates for him until the coming winter. The Imam told the *shawii* to store his sack in the date storage room and to mark it so that he would recognise it upon his return.

When the *shawii* returned for his sack of dates, he asked to be allowed into the store. The Imam told him that he could pick his sack up whenever he wanted.

Entering the store, the *shawii* found many sacks of good quality dates. He succumbed to temptation and took a sack of expensive dates known as *fardh*, instead of his own poor-quality dates. He split the sack into two portions and put them on the back of his donkey. Hurriedly, he left to return to his village.

Meanwhile, the Imam wanted to try some of his favourite *fardh* dates, so he went to the store to get some. To his surprise, he saw the *shawii's* sack in the store, while the sack of Fardh was missing. He asked the guard if the *shawii* had taken his sack of dates and was assured that he had done so.

The Imam realised that the *shawii* had taken the wrong sack and said, "Well, if the *shawii* took the sack of *fardh* by mistake, then may he enjoy it but if he intended to steal it, may the dates turn into stones!"

The *shawii* was hurrying towards his village and was about to arrive home. Suddenly, the sack and its content turned into stone and fell off the donkey's back. The sack can still be seen, split into two large stones, in Wadi Mistel.

THE TRACKER AND THE THIEF

This event took place during the reign of Imam Saif bin Sultan, when people became wealthy and safe from crime. A merchant arrived in Rustaq after dark and decided to sleep in the dry wadi. Exhausted from the long journey the merchant did not wake up when a thief came and stole his money.

Knowing that the Imam would employ the town's tracker to trace his footprints, the thief wisely split the money with the town tracker.

As the sun rose the merchant woke up to find himself with no money. He went to the Imam to tell him his story, and the Imam asked the tracker to follow the footprints of the thief and to bring him back as quickly as possible.

Soon the tracker returned claiming that the footprints had disappeared among those made by passing animals.

The Imam realised the tracker was lying and suspected that he might have struck a deal with the thief. So he said to him, "You have one month to find the thief. If you don't, you will face a severe penalty."

The tracker knew how uncompromising the Imam was when it came to dealing with thieves, and he began to look for the thief seriously. He found out that he had left Rustaq heading towards the Al Batinah coast, so he followed him.

At Widam Al Sahil, he was told that the thief had boarded a ship heading towards Makran. So the tracker boarded a ship to follow him.

In Makran, the tracker found him asleep under a tree and took the money from him. When he returned to Rustaq, the tracker went to his house to collect the rest of the stolen money, and then he went to the Imam and handed him the money, which was then returned to the merchant.

As for the tracker, he was imprisoned in the fort of Rustaq and, once again, people felt safe knowing that thieves are brought to justice.

THE HYENA AND THE COB OF CORN

In times long ago but not forgotten, there lived a ruler who chose the fort of Rustaq for his home. He had bells tied to a chain hanging from the roof so that anyone with a complaint could attract his attention. One dark night the bell rang waking everyone in the fort. The guards went to see the night caller and were awed to see a beast outside striking the ground with its leg.

They rushed to the ruler to tell him. The ruler told them to go and attend to the beast. When they did the beast signalled that they should follow her. They were shaking with fear as they returned to the ruler once again. He ordered three of the guards to follow and told them they had nothing to fear from supernatural forces as their fate was in the hands of the Almighty.

The beast galloped through the dead of night as the guards followed close on her heels through wadis and over mountains. Far from human habitation she stopped outside a cave and gestured for them to wait. She soon emerged with a baby cub whose throat was swollen as he gasped for breath. The beast withdrew as she placed her cub before them. What were they to do? It was obvious that the cub had a bone stuck in its throat. Delving into the animal's throat seemed a foolhardy and dangerous thing to do but an old and sagacious guard wisely suggested the strongest of them should strike the hyena in order to dislodge the

bone. The cub was taken unawares as the strike came and promptly the bone was ejected to the great relief of all.

The adult hyena was overcome with joy and gestured for the guards to wait as she re-entered the cave. When she emerged it was to present the guards with a corncob. As the guards left and withdrew from the entrance to the cave they discovered the cob was full of glittering gold.

At the fort the guards presented the ruler with the cob, who was as puzzled as he had not seen anything like it before.

No one could identify its origins until they remembered there was an old man who was reputedly more than two hundred years old. He might know where the cob came from.

Unfortunately the old man was senile and had lost his memory, but it was suggested his memory could be restored if a young woman would marry him and nurse him for two weeks.

The ruler offered a large reward to the woman who would consent to marry the old man. Finding such a woman proved a difficult task but eventually an agreeable young lady volunteered. Pampered and nursed for two weeks by the youthful hands of his wife the old man did indeed regain his memory. He identified the cob as the produce of a farm that had been established during the first years of human existence on earth, and the beast had emerged from the abyss of a time that had long since passed.

As for the wife, she lived happily with the old man until the day he died.

Rustaq fort

قلعة الرستاق

Sheikh Salem bin Mohammed bin Saqer Al Batthari told us the next three stories. The Al Battahira Bedouin live in the southern Al Wusta and Dhofar regions mainly in Shuwamiyah. The tribal name stems from *battha*, meaning sands, and is a reflection of their population in the past that multiplied and spread like the golden sands of the Rub Al Khali, the Empty Quarter.

DANCING WITH FIRE

Long ago in Shuwaymiyah there lived a beautiful woman called Shaifirah. Everyone, far and wide, knew of her wondrous dancing skills, which she had learned from her mother. In particular she excelled at the 'Naash' dance where women move their long hair in rhythm to the music.

One day members of a rival tribe, the Al Harasis, invited the Shuwaymiayah dancers to a wedding.

The dancing soon became a competition between the two tribes and it became clear that the Al Harasis were winning. Their best dancer, bint Budait, possessed far superior skills to any of the other women.

The Shuwaymiyah women did not want to accept defeat, and the Al Battahira reputation was at stake. The only sure way they knew of winning was to ask Shaifirah to dance. Shaifirah had given birth to a baby girl three days earlier and refused to take part as she was weak from childbirth and out of condition, but her proud sisters wouldn't take no for an answer. They pestered and pestered until finally Shaifirah gave in. She felt she had a moral obligation to compete to save the tribe's name from humiliation.

She quickly put on her dancing clothes, leapt on her camel and raced towards the contest. She looked like a woman possessed as she ordered her friends to light wood from the fire. She fastened the burning wood around her head and entered the dancing circle. Shaifirah began dancing and moving like nothing anyone had ever seen before. The burning wood in her long hair mesmerised the crowd, and both tribes surrounded her in awe, stunned by her beauty and talent. She flung herself into the ecstatic and fiery dance, finally slumping to the floor unconscious.

The contest was over. There was no question that the Al Battahira had won. Everyone agreed that Shaifirah should be crowned as the most talented and passionate dancer in the entire region.

THE KIDNAPPED ALI BIN HUZAIR

Long ago, like all children in his village, Ali bin Huzair used to play freely on the beach next to the sea. But times were changing. With the arrival of the Portuguese and their occupation of the main ports in Oman, the Shuwaymiyah coast was becoming a dangerous place. One day one of the Portuguese ships sailed up to the shore to get fresh supplies of water. When the ship sailed away, water was not the only thing they had taken. Ali had been kidnapped and was made to work for the enemy.

Over the years Ali learned the art of fighting and became a Portuguese soldier and pirate, and his knowledge of the language and geography of his homeland was an advantage to them in battle.

However Ali was only a child when he was kidnapped and he never really understood that the Portuguese were harming his own people, but as he grew older he began to fully understand the treachery of what he was doing and why it was wrong. He began to resent the Portuguese enemy. He yearned for his own family and village and kept planning how he could return home.

The opportunity arose one day when Ali was asked to see what ships he could find and plunder. He loaded his ship with gold coins and an ample supply of water, and food and set sail with his assistants. When night fell, Ali waited until the guards were asleep and followed the star known as "Yah" to reach his village. Whenever one of the sailors got up and asked Ali their whereabouts he told them to go back to sleep, that all was well.

When he reached Shuwaymiyah, his home, he took his sword and shield and entered the village. It was night but he soon found his parents' home and awakened them. His mother immediately recognised her beloved son.

Ali asked for the men of the village to be brought to his house. Then he told them his story and what he planned to do. The men of the village agreed and shortly before sunrise they boarded the ship and slaughtered the crew. They took the ship's cargo and divided the gold coins, food and water among the villagers.

Ali bin Huzair became a hero of the Al Battahira and lived in the village happily ever after.

Ali Bin Sharim Al Battahiri and the Tree

Ali was a leading fighter of the Al Battahira tribe long ago. One day a southern tribe known as the Bani Kathir attacked the Al Battahira. They were taken by surprise and lost almost all their camels and livestock. This took place while Ali, known for his strength, courage and fearless personality, was on a hunting expedition.

After the attack the tribe had to decide what to do. M'shailah, Ali's cousin, was a wiser and more tolerant man than Ali and believed diplomacy would spare the tribe a long war with the Bani Kathir. Under the leadership of M'shailah, the tribe mapped out a strategy for regaining their animals. M'sailah then gathered all the men and headed south towards the Bani Kathir but not before telling the remaining members of his tribe not to tell Ali of their plans.

Three days later Ali returned from his hunting to find the village had been destroyed and the camels, including his own camel, Farha, were missing. Blind with rage he asked his sister, Qbalat, what had happened. Eventually she gave in and told him the story and M'sailah's decision.

Ali immediately rode out after them. On his way he came across a large, old and gnarled tree. After he had rested under the shade of the tree he cut it and carrying it with him continued on his way.

When M'sailah arrived at the Bani Kathir settlement he immediately began to negotiate with them. He insisted on the return of all the stolen camels, but in the middle of the negotiations Ali suddenly arrived on the scene, raising his sword in one hand and the tree in the other. Fearing that Ali would ruin the peaceful negotiations, M'sailah ordered his men to arrest Ali, which they did, and he was tied with ropes against a tree.

That night Ali asked M'sailah about the progress of his negotiations. M'sailah told him the Bani Kathir would eventually return the camels but it would take some time. Ali grew more angry as he believed the Bani Kathir were not serious. At dawn Ali's tribesmen freed him and rallied around him to exact revenge on the Bani Kathir.

Ali carried his tree into battle. His enemies surrounded him and attempted to kill him but his fierceness and courage surprised them. They could not get past the tree that he used as a giant shield, and their swords and arrows missed their target and got stuck in it. After a bloody battle the Bani

Kathir retreated into the desert and acknowledged defeat. The Al Battahira collected their stolen camels to return home. Ali triumphantly rode Farha among the singing and dancing men.

After this incident the Al Battahira lived in peace and prosperity for many long years with Ali bin Sharim Al Battahiri as their hero. It is said that he alone, with the help of the tree, defeated the entire tribe of his enemies that numbered over one hundred.

THE MERCHANT'S BEAUTIFUL DAUGHTER

Muscat old town, the capital of Oman, extends along a bay between the imposing forts of Mirani and Jalali. When the Portuguese invaded the country in the 16th century they built Fort Mirani and considered it invincible. Imam Sultan bin Saif captured the fort from the Portuguese in 1649 through his outstanding leadership abilities coupled with the bravery and skill of his soldiers. According to legend however he had some extra help.

Narutem, an Indian merchant who supplied the fort with all provisions, had a very beautiful daughter. She had caught the eye of the Portuguese commander, Pereira, who wished to marry her. Narutem did not want his daughter, a Hindu, to marry Pereira, a Catholic. Alarmed, he refused permission.

Pereira was furious and he threatened to cancel the contracts Narutem had with the fort, which would mean Narutem's financial ruin. Narutem was worried and played for time. He pretended to change his mind and asked for a year to prepare for the wedding. Once agreement was reached he proceeded to tell Pereira that the fort would never stand a long siege. He claimed that the water in the tanks was foul and must be replaced. He said that the old stocks of wheat should be changed and the gunpowder removed and pounded. Pereira told him to go ahead, but when Narutem removed the items he didn't replace them.

Narutem knew Imam Sultan bin Saif was waiting for the right moment to attack the fort, and when he saw an opportunity to get rid of Pereira he informed Imam Sultan bin Saif that the garrison was weakened. The Imam launched his attack against the Portuguese and successfully took the fort. And so it is said that an affair of the heart played a part in the final expulsion of the Portuguese from Muscat and Oman.

THE SHY JINN

Yiti is a small fishing village east of Muscat and was relatively isolated until the advent of a recently built tarmac road. Essa Al Taie told us this tale.

A solitary rock stands close to the shoreline at Yiti, surrounded by the sea at high tide. Fishermen say that the rock suddenly appeared many, many years ago; one morning the villagers awoke it to find the rock in place. It was a different colour to the surrounding rocks and this, added to its sudden appearance, led the people to believe it was there as a result of divine intervention. Even though it was a difficult journey people travelled from far and wide to the rock as they believe it was inhabited by wise and good jinn, Sheikh Sam'un.

Sheikh Sam'un was believed by the people to work miracles, curing illnesses and solving problems. Childless women believed his spiritual intervention would help them conceive. Petitioners would bring clothes, goats and sweets as gifts and offerings for him. They would climb to the back of the rock for privacy and burn incense to ward off evil spirits before praying for help.

One day aircraft came and bombed the mountain, hoping to destroy it. Miraculously no bombs hit the target. The fishermen believe that Sheik Sam'un created a shield that made the bombs bounce off the mountain into the sea.
Now Sam'un has left the mountain. As roads have made

travelling from the capital easier more people have visited Yiti. Their behaviour is not always consistent with local custom. The fishermen say that the good and wise jinn has moved somewhere more secluded.

ZAHRAH

A'Seefa is a small fishing village along the coast from Yiti.
Essa Al Taie told this story.

Many years ago the villagers of A'Seefa were suffering from a prolonged drought. Their prayers for rain did not seem to be answered so they asked a beautiful girl in the village, Zahrah, to intercede with God on their behalf. Zahrah happily did so and was told that God would send rain but there was a price to pay. Zahrah would have to join him in the sky and become a shining star. When she agreed the drought was broken.

Now when the people of A'Seefa look into the sky at the brightest star they remember — Zahrah — her beauty and her sacrifice.

THE HOUSE OF GOLD

Wadi Tiwi, east of Muscat, runs down the Eastern Hajar mountains to the coast. Najeeb Al Taie told us this story.

High on a hill in Tiwi lie the crumbling remains of an imposing house, once the home of Ibn Mukarab, a rich man and poet from Eastern Saudi Arabia.

Ibn Mukarab had made enemies in his hometown as a result of which he had to run away. For a long time his enemies hunted and chased him for revenge, until he found refuge in Tiwi. There he built his house so high on a hill that he could see all those who approached. The house protected him from his avengers. However Ibn Mukarab wanted protection after death so he built a tomb in a cave on the opposite side of the wadi. The cave was very difficult to get to, so he built many steps so that his body could be carried there. Under each step he placed gold so that after his death the people would break the steps to find the gold. In this way there would be no trace of a path for his enemies to find his burial place.

SAVED BY ANGELS

Qalhat, near Tiwi, is one of the oldest towns and seaports in Oman but today only a trace of the city walls remain. Najeeb Al Taie told us this story.

That is with the exception of a ruined mausoleum that stands near the road. This is believed to be where Bibi Maryam was buried. Bibi Maryam was a religious and good woman and the past grandeur of her burial place reflects this. The building had a domed interior that was covered in the most beautiful coloured, glazed tiles. When a severe earthquake destroyed the town the building stood erect, and everyone believed that God had told his angels to protect the resting-place of Bibi Maryam.

SELMAH, THE BRAVE SHEPHERDESS

High on a remote plateau on Jabal Bani Jabir in the Eastern Hajar lies an extensive cave system. It includes the second largest cave chamber in the world. Near the entrance to the cave there is a qandilah, a shelter for goats and it is this that gives it its local name, Koshilat Maqandeli. More recently it has become known as Majlis al Jinn, meeting place of the spirits.

Scientists have ideas about how the cave system came into being but local people have their own tale to tell. Najeeb Altaie told us the story.

One day a young Bedouin woman, Selmah, left her goats safely in an enclosure while she went to fetch food. On her return she saw, to her horror, a leopard asleep over seven of her kid goats that he had killed. Selmah was enraged. She picked up a huge thistle plant and yelling fearlessly lifted her axe to attack the leopard. He retaliated by hitting at her body with one paw and blinding her with the other. As she fell she swung the axe and split the leopard's head down the middle. Her family found the two, dead in each other's arms.

To honour her bravery, God made seven stars fall from the sky creating seven *koshilat* or sinkholes.

THE MAGIC RING

Moqel cave lies close to Wadi Bani Khalid, a fertile and green area that has water flowing all year round. Bananas and dates grow in profusion and pools and streams make it a favoured place to live and popular tourist attraction.

Local people tell of a fissure in the mountain that used to open if you knew the right words. "Salim bin Saliym Salam" and the rock would open to reveal a beautiful paradise of gardens and cool streams. Najeeb Al Taie told us this story.

One day long ago a man uttered the magic words, "Salim bin Saliym Salam", so the rocks parted and he went inside. However he got lost in this beautiful paradise and, frightened, he wandered about aimlessly for some time until he met another man. This man had a magic ring that he said would guide the lost man out. The man lent the ring to the lost man and told him he must promise to leave it at the exit as he left. The lost man agreed but when he examined the ring he realised it was both beautiful and valuable. He decided to keep it. With the help of the ring he found the exit but as he climbed through, the rocks closed tightly around him. He was trapped there until the owner of the ring appeared and reminded him of his promise. The lost man said he was sorry and assured the owner of the ring he had indeed learned a lesson. With that the rocks parted and he was released.

THE MAGIC SWORD

High on Jabal Bani Jabir in the Eastern Hajar mountains lie 3,000-year-old tower tombs known locally as Burooj Kibaykib, the towers of Kibaykib. Najeeb Al Taie told us this story.

Kibaykib was a tyrant who built two massive towers for his own use. He was a giant of a man who owned a powerful, magic sword that could slice rocks in two with an explosion of light and fire. The people were afraid of him and wanted to get rid of him.

One day a Bedouin, Qadah, was walking through a wadi when he saw a pool Ayn Naghb. In the water was a beautiful woman so he hid behind a rock and watched her, entranced. When he made a sudden movement she spotted him and yelled that humans were not allowed there and demanded to know who had told him of the place. She threatened him by saying that her brother and father would kill him. He realised she was a jinn and begged her forgiveness and pardon. She calmed down but told him to leave and not return. She offered to tell him how he could kill Kibaykib and become a hero. Qadah was overjoyed and listened carefully. The jinn explained that if the tyrant was lying down with his eyes closed this meant he was really awake. However if his eyes were open he would be asleep and the magic sword could be seized. He must slice Kibaykib in two vertically to make sure he was dead. The jinn told Qadah where to find Kibaykib and off he went.

He crept up on Kibaykib and saw he had his eyes open and even though he was afraid of the tyrant he seized his sword. Before he could strike, Kibaykib awakened and fled to hide in a cave far away. Qadah pursued him and when he caught up with him, he struck him and cut him in half with the magic sword. Unfortunately in his fear and trembling he sliced him in half horizontally. His head and shoulders fell to the ground but the lower part of his body ran a long way before it fell dead. That is why Kibaykib needed two tombs some distance apart.

THE MAN WHO CARRIED HIS PARENTS

Told to Essa Al Taie by Mohammed bin Zaher Al Maashiry from Al Amrat. Amrat is a foothill village in Wadi Adai, the long narrow wadi on the route from Muscat to Quriyat on the coast.

There was a good young man who cared for his elderly and demanding parents. They were so frail he had to carry them around everywhere with him. He made extra large mats out of strong palm branches, one for each of them. Then he made a yoke and harness for around his shoulders and neck so that he could bear their weight. With one parent on either side he went about his business.

One day, to his absolute horror, he heard them plotting to eat him, and from their conversation, and for the first time, he realised they were *sa'hara*, sorcerers. He didn't know what to do and turned to the Holy Prophet Mohammed (PBUH) for advice.

The Holy Prophet listened to the problem carefully and then advised him. He could do what he wished with his father, even kill him if his own life was threatened, however whatever his mother did to him, be it kill him, eat him or whatever, he must not harm a hair of her head. Mohammed told the man that the tie with his mother, like the umbilical cord, was so strong it could never be broken.

THE ANGELS WHISPER

Told to Essa Al Taie by Mohammed bin Zaher Al Mashry from Al Amerat.

One day in the mosque a man was waiting for the religious leader, the Imam, and his assistant, the muezzin, who called the faithful to prayer. As he waited he heard the angels whispering above him. They were talking about a child who had just been born in the village. He listened carefully and apprehensively, as his own wife was due to give birth. The angels said that the child would do great harm.

When the Imam and Muezzin arrived they said that they had been delayed helping a woman who was having trouble delivering a boy child. The man was horrified as he realised it was his wife they were talking about and his own son.

When he returned home he was determined to act and stop the baby growing up to do harm. He took the baby and placed him out on the hillside far away from the village. He told his tearful wife they must never, never talk about the child again.

The *shawawi*, shepherds who lived outside the village, found the baby and raised him as their own. Time passed and when the boy grew up he asked permission to seek work in the village so that he could earn some money. The *shawawi* were reluctant to allow him to go as they wanted him to be one of them. However he was so insistent that they finally agreed. They took him to the market place where a farmer and his wife were looking for someone to help on their farm. The *shawawi* agreed he could work on the farm with the condition that he must return at the end of each day to live with them.

One dreadful day something came over the young man, he picked up a large axe, attacked and mercilessly killed the farmer. As this happened in the fields nobody knew who had committed the terrible crime. Now the farmer's wife asked the young man to come and live with her as she needed much more help with the farm. Again the *shawawi* reluctantly agreed, and after a time the pair got married.

One day as the young man was removing his shirt the woman froze in horror. There was a distinctive and unmistakable birthmark on his shoulder. She had seen an identical birthmark once before. Instantly she knew this man was her son. Distraught and overcome with what had happened she killed herself.

THE WATER DIVINER

Told by Sheikh Ishaq Al Kindi of Al Amerat

Once upon a time there was a man called Al Sarkhi, renowned throughout Oman for tracking sources of underground water and discovering the right places to dig wells for *aflaj*.

One day, the Imam called him and demanded to know the secret of Al Sarkhi's knowledge.

He replied by saying, "If anyone else had asked me I wouldn't tell them, but I cannot hide anything from you now that you've asked me."

When I was young, I used to go hunting. I would spend two to four days in the mountains, plains and wadis. One day I saw an old man sleeping under the shade of a tree. He looked tired and ill.

He woke up and asked me, in a faint voice, to approach him. "Give me some water and dates, I feel ill and unable to move."

So I gave him water and dates, and he drank and ate. Then he asked me to pass by and bring him food and water. I returned to the old man and brought him food and water.

On the third day, he felt better and said, "You have done me a great favour and I want to repay you."

"You look tired and poor, how are you going to repay me? I think you had better come to my village where you will be my guest until you feel better."

He asked me to come closer and when I did, he put some kohl on my eyelids. When I opened my eyes I began to see what lies underground, minerals, water and so on.

I described what I saw, so he asked me to come closer. He then put kohl on my eyelids again. When I opened my eyes, my sight was sharp but slightly less than it had been.

He put the kohl on for the third time, and this time I saw only water underground.

When I told the old man he said, "This will do you good and people will also benefit from it. The things you saw before are of no use to either you or others."

From that day on I have been helping people bring their villages and farms to life again."

THE BRAVE IMAM

The historically important town of Nizwa developed alongside the course of two wadis, Abyadh and Kalbouh. The grave and mosque of Imam Warith bin Ka'ab lies alongside Wadi Kalbouh.

Imam Warith bin Ka'ab hailed from Al Hajar in Wadi bani Kharous. Tales abound about his quest for justice and equality. One day he heard a voice commanding him to go to Nizwa, which was ruled by a tyrant, and restore justice in the town, so he and his brother travelled to there. Warith bravely defeated the tyrant in battle and was elected Imam by the religious leaders of Nizwa in 801 AD.

He was as brave in his death as he was in his rule. As Imam, Warith had imprisoned a group of petty criminals in a small cell in the middle of Wadi Kalbouh. One day heavy torrential rain began to fall. As the wadi flooded, the Imam and his guards rushed to rescue the prisoners. They were too late, the waters had swept away the prisoners and destroyed the prison. The current in the wadi was so strong that the Imam and his guards were drowned in the rescue attempt along with the prisoners.

THE CAMELS MOVED

Nizwa's most famous aflaj *(irrigation channel) is Falaj Daris. Close by the falaj behind Harrat Al Kinud district is a small mosque, Masjid Al Hasat, in the shadow of a massive rock. Told by Halimma bint Said AlKindi.*

Hamad bin Abdulla Al Kindi was a Sufi, a Muslim mystic, reputed to have great powers. Legend has it that one day he guided a massive rock down the mountain with the aid of a single alfalfa leaf. When the Imam heard the story he ordered a mosque to be built as a record of the miracle.

Hamad was completely devout and spent all his time worshipping alone in the mosque. His father used to worry about his welfare and wonder what he did with his time.

One day he came quietly to the mosque to look inside. He got the surprise of his life. Hamad was reciting the Holy Qur'an while making a caravan of camels from tree leaves. The caravan of camels was 'moving' around him in a circle one by one. His father was shocked but recognising his son's power and devotion decided not to spy on him again.

THE BEWITCHED GIRL

Abdullah bin Humaid Al Salmi was a famous theologist and poet and one of Oman's most distinguished scholars. His most famous book, Tuhfat Al Ayan, records many historical tales including the following two. The story of The Bewitched Girl is recorded in the form of a narrative qasidah, a long form of poem. It begins by categorising the story as a miracle.

A noble young girl of Nizwa died when she was just nine years of age. The day after she was buried a shepherd passing by the cemetery noticed her grave was empty.

Time passed by until one day the girl's mother was visiting a family of Bedouin who lived on the edge of the village. She was shocked to recognise her daughter playing happily with other children. She rushed towards her joyfully and identified herself but the girl did not know her. A Bedouin woman approached the mother and asked her to leave the girl, her daughter, alone.

Each claiming the girl was hers the women approached the local judge.

He listened to the statements of both women. "Stay awake all night and tomorrow morning I want you to tell me about the planet of Venus."

In the morning both women were brought before the judge who asked for their observations.

"It moved from the far right of the moon to the far left, Your Honour," said the Bedouin woman.

"By the name of Allah and His Prophet Mohammed, Your Honour, the planet hardly left its position next to the moon," said the other woman.

It was obvious to the judge that the second woman had stayed up all night for the love of her daughter while the Bedouin woman slept.

The judge ordered the custody of the girl should be given back to her real mother, whereupon they returned home for a joyful reunion.

SULAIMAH BIN MALIK

From the book Tuhfat Alayan by Noor Aldeen AlSalmi

Malik bin Faham fathered many sons but he favoured Sulaimah, the youngest, more than the others. This led to Sulaimah's brothers envying him, which disturbed Malik. Each night Malik chose one of his sons to guard his citadel, and the brothers hatched a plot to ruin Sulaimah's favoured position. They told their father that he frequently fell asleep on duty and was not reliable. Malik did not believe them and told them so but over time he began to doubt Sulaimah.

One night Malik crept out of his palace to see whether Sulaimah was awake on guard duty. He made his way to where Sulaimah was on duty. Sulaimah, on horseback, had fallen asleep, however as the horse sensed Malik's stealthy approach, it neighed, alerting Sulaimah to danger.

Immediately Sulaimah reacted by firing an arrow at the intruder unaware it was his own father. Malik was killed and Sulaimah fled Oman to escape the wrath of his brothers.

He kept his tribal name and travelled to Persia. The Persians loathed their tyrannical king and enlisted Sulaimah's help to overthrow him. Sulaimah agreed and planned a huge wedding as part of his plot. He acted the role of the bride but when the tyrant came to claim a night with the bride as his right, he found Sulaimah. The plan was a success as Sulaimah killed the king and the Persians, delighted to be free from his unstable and violent rule, crowned Sulaimah their king. Sulaimah, with the help of his brother, Hina'h, reigned for many years until his death.

THE FLYING MOSQUE

The following three stories told by Najeeb Al Taie

Just before Buhla, on the road from Nizwa, there used to be a village outside the city wall. It is said to have mysteriously disappeared many years ago and all that remains are the ruins of three small mosques, Masjid Al Ubad, mosques of the saints.

According to local legend the mosque on the highest hill flew from Rustaq to the village one night. Hence it is known as Al Taier, the flying mosque.

THE CHAINED TREE

In the centre of Buhla souq a splendid old tree gives shade to people and animals alike. Water pots hang from the tree to assuage the thirst of passers by. Nowadays the chains around the tree serve the purpose of a place to tie animals for sale.

This was not always the case. Buhla people believed that jinn lived in the tree and that they were not always friendly. They chained the tree down to stop the jinn flying away.

THE BESIEGED BROTHER

Jabrin Castle lies on a sand and gravel plain many miles away from the nearest town of Buhla. It seems an unusual place to build such an impressive fortified castle. It was the home of Imam Bil'Arab bin Sultan, a scholarly and generous ruler in the 17th century. Disliking town life he built Jabrin Castle so that he could live and rule from a situation of peace and quiet. He opened a school and was surrounded by poets, philosophers and artists. One of his interests was astronomy and there are two rooms in the castle that are called the Sun and Moon rooms. The delicate plasterwork and painted ceilings of the fort are justifiably famous for their intricate workmanship and beauty.

Unfortunately Bil'Arab's brother Saif fought with him over leadership of the country and had himself declared Imam when Bil'Arab was still alive. Saif took control over the fortified buildings in the area, one by one, until his brother was besieged at Jabrin. Bil'Arab knew his people were suffering and realising that he couldn't win, prayed to God for deliverance. The next morning he was found dead. He lies buried inside Jabrin Castle.

THE THYME HERB PLANT

Essa Al Taie told this tale that comes from Jabal Akhdar the green mountain, famous for orchards and plants. Roses grown there are made into rose water, valued highly in Oman.

Long ago in a village on top of Jabal Al Akhdar, a man was struck by an unknown illness. No one knew how to cure him. Saddened and desperate to save him, his family took him to Madinah to see the Holy Prophet Mohammed (PBUH).

When they saw the Holy Prophet, they explained the man's ordeal and his symptoms. The Holy Prophet asked them where they came from.

"From Oman," they replied, "from the Jabal Al Akhdar."

The Prophet looked at them and told them about an herbal plant called thyme that grows there that would cure him. They should boil the thyme leaves and give him the juice to drink. God willing, he would be cured.

Happy and eager to try the prescription, the family returned home. They gathered the leaves of the plant, boiled them and gave the juice to the ailing man. Gradually, the man felt better, but he was still not completely cured.

And so the family returned to Madinah to see the Prophet once again. Wondering why the man had not been cured, the Prophet asked them to bring him the plant.

When the plant was brought to the Prophet, he asked it why it had not cured the man.

The plant replied saying, "I ask for your forgiveness, but I have cured him from 99 ailments and there is only one left from which I cannot save him ... death."

THE SOLID GHEE

Story told to Amina Alrabia' by her grandmother, Arous Awlad Yaqout, from Salalah. Salalah is in Dhofar, the southernmost region of Oman.

An old man and his wife wanted to make the dish *asseedah* when they realised they didn't have enough ghee because they couldn't afford to buy it.

"What do you think we should do now?" the old woman asked her husband.

"I don't know, replied the husband."

"Didn't you go to market this morning?" she continued.

"Yes, he said, "I went to the market but I didn't have any money."

His wife asked, "Do you remember where the shop is?"

"I do, and I'll tell you what we'll do. First cover yourself with a shawl and hide a small pot under it. I will pretend to hit you with a stick as we enter the souq and you pretend to cry. I will keep on pretending until we get to the shop."

"Oh dear, I suppose there is no other way to get the ghee," his wife replied.

Just before they went into the souq the old lady started screaming, "Oh man, you have tortured me and made my life a misery."

"Well, you don't obey me and you don't do anything useful," he shouted.

As they entered the souq, still shouting, a crowd began to gather around.

"Old man, why are you doing this to her?" they asked.

"This old lady is bad to us all; she sleeps all day and doesn't do any work."

"Then let her go back to her family," they said.

"No, she must come back home with me," he responded.

"But what if she doesn't want to go home with you?"

"She must, she must," the old man shouted.

When they arrived at the shop the old women sat at the entrance and started crying and howling louder. "This man has made my life a misery, she told the shopkeeper, please help me."

"Aren't you ashamed of yourself, old man? Beating your wife at your age, she is the mother of your children, why are you doing this to her"?

The old man responded angrily, "Don't interfere, she won't obey my orders and she's not a nice woman anymore."

The shopkeeper told the old lady to go and sit in the shop while he talked to her husband and tried to calm him down. She entered the shop, closed the door and looked for the ghee.

Outside her husband was shouting at the shopkeeper, "Tell her to come out and come home with me."

"She will not come out unless she wants to."

Meanwhile the old lady had found the ghee but it was solid and wouldn't pour into her pot. She shouted to her husband, "You be quiet out there, you son of the solid ghee."

He quickly yelled back, "Oh I'm the son of the solid ghee am I? Then I'll have to use my stick again."

She understood his message and took a stick from the shop and stirred the ghee until it was soft and she could fill her pot.

The old man allowed the shopkeeper to calm him and the shopkeeper called to the old lady to come outside and be reunited with her husband. "Go home together, he will not harm you if you do as he says," he told the wife.

"If you hit her she will complain to the judge" he told the husband.

"No, I won't do that," replied the husband, "let's go home, wife."

They left and as she took the ghee out from under her shawl he said, "It's good you shouted that message to me from the shop otherwise we couldn't make *asseedah*."

"When I found the ghee solid I didn't know what to do. I'm glad you told me to use a stick. Now we can eat."

They made the *asseedah*, ate it and were happy.

When the shopkeeper opened up the next day and a customer came for ghee he realised it had been stolen. "Who has taken my ghee?" he screamed.

"Maybe there's a hole in the dish and it's dripped away," said the customer.

"No, look there isn't a hole. Who has stolen my ghee?" he shouted.

A crowd gathered. "Did you sell any yesterday, did anyone visit your shop?" they questioned.

"No, I didn't sell any yesterday and no one came to the shop except the old couple. She came inside while I calmed her husband down."

"Then it must have been them. Do you know them, would you recognise them again?" came from the crowd.

"Only if I see them," said the unhappy shopkeeper.

"Well they've certainly played a trick on you. They came, took the ghee and disappeared."

For three days everyone searched for the couple but with no success.

BIBLIOGRAPHY

Abdullah ibn Humaid as Salimi, Tuhfat al Ayan bi-sirat Ahl'Uman

Muhammed ibn Abdulla as Salimi, Nahdat al-Ayan bi-hurriyat 'Uman

Hatim Al Taie, Joan Pickersgill, Nasser Al Taie, Oman: A Comprehensive Guide to the Sultanate of Oman, Al Roya Publishing, 1997

Joan Pickersgill, Muscat, The Jewel of Arabia, Al Roya Publishing, 1998

Philip Ward, Travels in Oman: On The Track of The Early Explorers, Oleander Press, 1987

The Authors

Hatim Al Taie founded Al Roya Press and Publishing House 15 years ago. He specialises in publishing books and magazines that promote Oman.

Hatim is an accomplished writer who is keen to explore his culture and its roots. *Omani Folk Tales* represents his strong desire to record traditional narrative before it vanishes.

Joan Pickersgill first visited Oman in 1991 and lived there for 12 years. Her love of Oman's natural beauty led to extensive travel in the more remote parts of the country. She has written two guidebooks on the Sultanate and contributed to magazines in Oman, the Emirates and Britain. Her interest in the country's heritage and culture motivated her work on *Omani Folk Tales.*

Since graduating from Surrey Institute of Art and Design with a 1st class honours degree, James Norton has been involved with art and architectural museum and exhibition projects worldwide. He is currently working on an exhibition of landscape paintings and developing design ideas for the Royal Museum of Scotland and the Natural History Museum in London. His other work includes painting, drawing, illustration, 3-dimensional design, music and film.